ANDREW WYETH

AN EXHIBITION ORGANIZED BY

PENNSYLVANIA ACADEMY OF THE FINE ARTS

ANDREW WYETH

TEMPERAS · WATERCOLORS · DRY BRUSH · DRAWINGS · 1938 into 1966

PENNSYLVANIA ACADEMY OF THE FINE ARTS, PHILADELPHIA, OCTOBER 8–NOVEMBER 27, 1966

BALTIMORE MUSEUM OF ART, DECEMBER 13, 1966–JANUARY 22, 1967

WHITNEY MUSEUM OF AMERICAN ART, NEW YORK, FEBRUARY 14–APRIL 2, 1967

THE ART INSTITUTE OF CHICAGO, APRIL 21–JUNE 4, 1967

©1966, Pennsylvania Academy of the Fine Arts

Library of Congress Catalog Card Number 66-27597

Published by Abercrombie & Fitch Co., New York

Second Printing, November 1966

FOREWORD

Successive exhibitions are the everyday life of museums, which display contemporary, ancient, or exotic art intended to sharpen our aesthetic sensibilities. Treasures from many lands and diverse ages may stimulate our imaginations and enable us, in some degree, to transcend the limitations of time and place. Sometimes, however, as on the present occasion, the most moving artistic experience is that in which we encounter genius on our own doorsteps and realize that the objects of our own familiar world can be transmuted into the highest realm of art.

The Pennsylvania Academy of the Fine Arts, long ambitious to present a truly definitive and retrospective exhibition of the work of Andrew Wyeth, is singularly fortunate, now, in that the artist himself has made this coveted honor possible. With characteristic loyalty, Wyeth, whose work enjoys universal acclaim, chose his home state as the locale for the original showing of his most significant exhibition, and the Academy, with its impressively long history of supporting American art, as the institution to organize and initially present the show. To an institution of brave accomplishment but small staff the challenge was of giant proportions, but the Academy eagerly welcomed the opportunity offered, and as this Foreword is being written a great and beautiful exhibition is assured.

Our very first thanks go to Mr. and Mrs. Andrew Wyeth for help of incalculable importance. Working with them both, as we endeavored to carry out the artist's wishes concerning the content and significance of his exhibition, has been an unusually happy and memorable experience. To Mrs. Wyeth we add a special note of gratitude for making available certain important records which she has had the interest and perception to gather over the years, and which now enhance this catalogue.

We are heavily indebted to all of the lenders for their generosity in sharing valuable and cherished possessions. Their sacrifice is genuine for, in a majority of cases, the owners will be deprived of their works of art for a period of some months while the exhibition is shown by the four collaborating museums. In a few instances, and for completely understandable reasons, permissions could not be granted for the entire number of museums on the circuit. The catalogue listings indicate these limited showings.

An exhibition comprising so many of the finest examples of work by Andrew Wyeth called for a catalogue worthy of the collection it was to record and memorialize. We are most fortunate in having Dr. Edgar P. Richardson, art historian and critic, as the writer of the text and catalogue notes. On Dr. Richardson's advice the listing has been arranged chronologically. This plan draws attention to a steady development of the artist through his early years of training under his father, N. C. Wyeth, distinguished artist-illustrator, and stresses present achievements as represented by recent works. Many of the latter are now shown for the first time.

When we selected a publisher and approached the intricacies of actual catalogue production a happy association developed as we began to work closely with Charles A. Pearce, publisher of Abercrombie & Fitch books. Mr. Pearce has given us understanding, as well as highly technical assistance.

On the very difficult problem of the fidelity of our illustrations—a major concern—it has been our good fortune to have as an adviser and friend, Richard Meryman, staff writer for LIFE and author of an authoritative article on Wyeth for that magazine. We have benefited greatly from his knowledge and experience.

As the Wyeth exhibition began to take shape its scope and importance dictated that it should reach as large an audience as possible and not be restricted to our own institution. Three important museums immediately expressed a wish to be included in the arrangements and their sustained enthusiasm has been of great encouragement all along the way. To their directors we express particular appreciation: Lloyd Goodrich of the Whitney Museum of American Art in New York; Charles P. Parkhurst of the Baltimore Museum of Art; John Maxon of the Art Institute of Chicago.

It would have been quite impossible to undertake so complex an organization as that of the present show without the ready and generous assistance of the artist's dealer, M. Knoedler & Company, represented specifically by Coe Kerr. To him and to his able assistant, Miss Hazel Oxholm, we record our grateful appreciation.

It is a pleasure to report the gracious and individual help of several friends of the Academy. Mrs. Chester Dale of New York City spontaneously altered exhibition plans of her own so that conflicts of interest might be avoided. Bernard A. Bergman of Philadelphia gave us expert guidance in the realm of public relations. A lender to the exhibition—Mrs. Lee C. Schlesinger of Metairie, Louisiana—added a contribution as heartwarming as it was unexpected. It is a happy circumstance that we have been able to draw upon the skills and creative imagination of Raymond A. Ballinger, designer of this catalogue. It has been stimulating to work with him.

My own staff at the Academy must not be forgotten as these grateful and sincere thanks are recorded. To my own assistant, Mrs. Loren Eiseley, to my secretary, Mrs. Dorothy E. Runk, and to Mrs. Margaret R. Fischer, especially engaged to assist with this project, I give much praise.

JOSEPH T. FRASER, JR.
Director
Pennsylvania Academy of the Fine Arts

As this catalogue goes to press a notification has been received from the Catherwood Foundation of Bryn Mawr, Pa., of a generous grant to the Pennsylvania Academy of the Fine Arts to assist in this publication. We are exceedingly grateful.

LENDERS TO THE EXHIBITION

Addison Gallery of American Art
Mrs. and Mrs. Walter H. Annenberg
Art Institute of Chicago
Mr. and Mrs. Lester Avnet
Dr. Catherine Bacon
Mr. Smith W. Bagley
Mr. and Mrs. Courtlandt D. Barnes
Miss Amanda K. Berls
Mrs. Alfred E. Bissell
Mr. and Mrs. Stephen W. Blodgett
Mr. and Mrs. Robert Blum
Mr. and Mrs. J. Bruce Bredin
Mrs. Henry W. Breyer, Jr.
Mrs. Charles Brisk
Mr. Tate Brown
California Palace of The Legion of Honor
Mr. W. S. Carpenter, Jr.
Cincinnati Art Museum
City Art Museum of St. Louis
Mrs. Ledyard Cogswell
Colby College Art Museum
Mr. Loring W. Coleman
W. B. Connor Foundation
Mr. and Mrs. William S. Cook
Mr. William Coolidge
Currier Gallery of Art
Mr. Stephen Currier
Dallas Museum of Fine Arts
Mr. and Mrs. Courtlandt P. Dixon
Hotel du Pont
Mrs. Stephen Etnier
Mr. and Mrs. Marshall Field, III
Mr. and Mrs. Roger S. Firestone
Mr. and Mrs. James Fosburgh
Mr. and Mrs. Raymond French
Mr. and Mrs. Edward Gerry

Mr. and Mrs. Henry Sage Goodwin
Mr. and Mrs. Lloyd Goodrich
Mr. and Mrs. George Greenspan
Mrs. John S. Griswold
Dr. Margaret I. Handy
Mr. and Mrs. T. Edward Hanley
Mr. and Mrs. Harry G. Haskell, Jr.
Mr. and Mrs. J. Welles Henderson
Mrs. John H. Hinman
Joseph H. Hirshhorn Collection
Mr. and Mrs. Philip Hofer
Mr. and Mrs. Oscar B. Huffman
Mrs. B. Brewster Jennings
Mr. and Mrs. Nelson R. Kandel
Mrs. Thomas S. Kelly
M. Knoedler & Company, Inc.
Mr. and Mrs. Kenneth Morse Kurson
Mr. and Mrs. John T. Landreth
Dr. and Mrs. Louis Lapid
Mrs. Frederick H. Lassiter
Mr. and Mrs. Alexander M. Laughlin
Mr. Halleck Lefferts
Mrs. Madison H. Lewis
Mr. and Mrs. Henry Loeb
Lyman Allyn Museum
Mr. and Mrs. John D. MacDonald
Mr. and Mrs. Eugene McDermott
Mrs. Josiah Marvel
Mrs. Charles B. Mayer
Mr. and Mrs. Roger Milliken
Mr. and Mrs. Robert Montgomery
Professor and Mrs. Charles H. Morgan
Mr. and Mrs. Samuel F. B. Morse
Museum of Fine Arts, Boston
Museum of Fine Arts, Houston
Museum of Modern Art

National Gallery of Oslo, Norway
New Britain Museum of American Art
Mr. and Mrs. Leslie P. Ogden
Mrs. Charles S. Payson
Pennsylvania Academy of the Fine Arts
Philadelphia Museum of Art
Mr. and Mrs. Lee E. Phillips, Jr.
Mr. Parker Poe
Mr. and Mrs. Joseph Verner Reed
Mr. and Mrs. W. Glasgow Reynolds
Mr. and Mrs. Vincent de Roulet
Mrs. Lee C. Schlesinger
Mr. Benno Schmidt
Dr. and Mrs. James Semans
Shelburne Museum
Mrs. Paul E. Shorb
Mr. Gordon M. Smith
Mr. Robert H. Smith
Mr. Stanley S. Snellenburg
Mr. and Mrs. Andrew J. Sordoni, Jr.
Mr. and Mrs. Robert W. Stoddard
Mr. and Mrs. Robert L. B. Tobin
Virginia Museum of Fine Arts
Wadsworth Atheneum
Mr. and Mrs. Norton S. Walbridge
Mr. and Mrs. John Warner, 3rd
Mr. and Mrs. William E. Weiss, Jr.
Mr. and Mrs. Richard S. West
William A. Farnsworth Library & Art Museum
Wilmington Society of the Fine Arts
Mrs. Coleman Woolworth
Mrs. Norman B. Woolworth
Mr. James H. Worth
Mr. and Mrs. William A. Worth
Mr. and Mrs. Andrew Wyeth
and nine anonymous lenders

THE ARTIST: HIS LIFE AND WORK

After more than half a century of art built on a rejection of nature, our age is not well equipped to understand the painter's use of imaginative observation. This catalogue attempts, therefore, to go beyond a listing of titles, dimensions, and names of owners of the pictures exhibited, to show something of their sources and of the transformation worked upon those sources.

Andrew Wyeth's art is an art of observation, selection, and the intensifying effect of memory, affection, and power of vivid statement. "It is not the country," he observed, as we were talking of one of the pictures in this exhibition, "but what you carry to it that makes an artist."

What Wyeth brings to his subject is not only a remarkably disciplined skill but an involvement which (more than his skill) requires explanation. Not merely an esthetic dogma or a theory of painting but his whole life and personality are reflected in his art, and the observer must, consciously or unconsciously, recognize this strong sense of identification which, far more than realistic detail, distinguishes Wyeth's work from that of prevailing trends in painting.

Almost every picture in this exhibition takes its departure from something seen either in Chadds Ford or in Cushing, Maine. It is remarkable that Andrew Wyeth has found continuing sources of inspiration for thirty years of painting from such a small portion of the earth's surface. In Chadds Ford he has drawn his subjects from a stretch of about two miles of the Brandywine valley and a similar distance up the side valley of Harvey Run. In Maine, over hardly a greater distance, his subjects are found up and down the Georges River. The few not drawn literally from home ground, are of nearby places.

"You know," said a well-meaning but obtuse friend of Wyeth to me, "people think Andy paints the country around his home; but when you go there, it isn't like that at all." The artist himself commented on this effect once from another point of view. "I used to take people to see the places where their pictures were done but I don't anymore, because I found they were always disappointed." What they missed, of course, seeing the subject for themselves, was the artist's eye, his mind, and his power to translate simple objects to another plane of feeling.

"I have to find the reason for painting a thing," he says. "That is what makes an indelible impression." The hills he paints are those he has tramped over every day of his life; the Chadds Ford farmhouses are those he has known all his life. He has been in their rooms, looked from their windows. He has eaten lunches there with the families and drunk their cider, sat talking with them about country matters. Finally some trivial incident—a sudden wind blowing the curtains when a window is opened to cool a hot room—or a gleam of late afternoon sun upon a whitewashed wall will catch his attention, and this momentary experience will crystallize the associations of a lifetime. The painting made of that moment contains the meaning of a day, a place, a season of the year, a phase of America.

Karl Kuerner's house and farm; Adam Johnson, the Lopers and other Negro citizens of Chadds Ford; the Olsons and their house in Maine; Henry Teel's house, his island, his boat—these subjects Wyeth has painted again and again. Every one of these pictures has resulted from some small incident, but the incident has been transformed by feelings distilled from a thousand days of living and remembering. Wyeth has no need for multiple images or any such complicated device; years of association are condensed into a single image.

Another factor, perhaps, enters into the haunting quality of his pictures. In the last hundred years our civilization has passed through a long period of looking outward. The steamship, the railroad, the camera, the airplane have opened to us the entire globe. We have been absorbed in learning the meaning of Europe and the Orient, of the Near East, of Africa and the South Seas. Another flood of impressions has poured into our minds from the past ages which the science of archaeology has raised ghostlike from the earth. The arts of many ancient, exotic, and primitive peoples have been brought into our museums and homes and have become part of our minds.

Our art has paused in its own inner development to take in all these intoxicating impressions. Undoubtedly we have learned much. It is too soon to say how deep-rooted and lasting may be the works of art that describe this experience; it is enough to say that we have been bathed and saturated in it.

But art arises in the human spirit beyond the reach of words, from the levels of deepest memories. We are creatures who need the near and the familiar as well as the exotic. Emerson, a pioneer in American study of Eastern thought, wrote in his journal (June 8, 1838): "A man must have aunts and cousins, must buy carrots and turnips, must have barn and woodshed, must go to market and to the blacksmith's shop, must saunter and sleep and be inferior and silly."

Something of the refreshing quality of Andrew Wyeth's work comes, I believe, from the circumstance that it deals with memories of life in our own land; that it gives us the truths of home with remarkable eloquence. We respond, as to a voice speaking to us of our half-forgotten selves.

I. *THE PREPARATION*

It has been a long journey for Wyeth to come to this point. Born in Chadds Ford, Pennsylvania, in 1917, he was the son of the gifted and successful illustrator, N. C. Wyeth. A delicate child, Andrew was educated at home and trained by his father who subjected him to a severely disciplined apprenticeship in the studio. N. C. Wyeth, a highly skillful draughtsman, had mastered the anatomy of the human body so that he could draw any scene of action, any kind of violent movement, without referring to a model.

He made his son draw from casts and study Rimmer's Anatomy, drilled him to study a model, then to turn his back and draw the figure from memory. "Andy," he said, "I want you to learn to draw so that when you want to express yourself you won't fumble." He trained him to paint still life, saying, "When you're doing that form and shadow, remember it is not just a shadow, it is something that will never happen again just like that. Try to get that quality, that fleeting character of the thing."

This diligent training of a natural gift produced an exceptional facility of hand and eye to record the visible world with an ease which the artist later came to believe dangerous. His first watercolors were painted with a kind of explosive impressionism. Effects of light and movement, water and sun, are set down in them with the greatest speed and dash; they are full of the exuberance of life and joy in the out-of-doors. His development in style has been an effort to discipline this exceptional facility to serve what he calls "the truth of the object."

The paintings in tempera are the mileposts of this development. Tempera, an exacting medium, has its own technique which demands time and patience as well as skill. Dry mineral pigments, ground to a fine powder, are mixed with yolk of egg and thinned with water; the paint is then laid on in strokes of a fine watercolor brush. The medium is a sympathetic one for a draughtsman, for, while the hand really draws in delicate strokes of color, tempera is capable of the aerial effects of light and air which form so much of the poetry of Wyeth's vision of the world.

Wyeth learned the use of tempera from his brother-in-law, Peter Hurd, who had studied under N. C. Wyeth in 1924-1926 and married his daughter, Henriette Wyeth, the portrait painter, in 1929. Although Peter Hurd has made his home in New Mexico, he and his wife are often in Chadds Ford. In the nineteen-thirties, Hurd, like many artists, was searching after new (or rather old) techniques, and painted in tempera and fresco. Andrew Wyeth tried both and settled upon tempera.

The works included in the present exhibition have been arranged in the order of execution so far as can be determined by Mrs. Wyeth from her own careful records and from the artist's excellent memory. It is interesting to see how subjects appear and reappear in his work, and with what subtle differences of treatment the same themes are handled at different periods.

The record is important in another way for our understanding of his work. Wyeth builds up his temperas so slowly that sometimes he works on one almost through the round of the seasons. What appears to be an instantaneous flash of observation has been thought about and matured during months of work. One can see that details at first central to the idea fade gradually away and are eliminated. Watercolors of other subjects are done while work on a tempera goes forward.

This will not surprise anyone who knows how painters worked in the past. But artists using their imagination upon nature are so few today that the poetic quality of Wyeth's realism and the sustained, disciplined, conscious effort that create these images of an instant of experience, need to be insisted upon; this is important for our understanding of the artist's achievement.

II. *THE FIRST PHASE*

The earliest examples of Andrew Wyeth's work I have seen are pen-and-ink head and tail pieces to an essay written by his father, a recollection of Howard Pyle, in the Brandywine Edition of Pyle's *The Merry Adventures of Robin Hood* (Scribner's, 1933). An editor's note explains that these were drawn by N. C. Wyeth's "twelve-year-old son Andrew," which puts them in the year 1929. The precision and decorative elegance of line learned from the Howard Pyle tradition were, and are a basic element of his style.

His growth toward an art of air and light was an instinctive development. Still doing knights and soldiers, he turned from pen-and-ink to the use of pencil and colored washes, then to watercolor drawings in which the Negro citizens of Chadds Ford made their first appearance. When he saw Winslow Homer's watercolors, at about age sixteen, they helped him to move in a direction he had already discovered, toward a bold, rapid impression of light and tone. Precision in drawing, an eye for light and tone, were the two poles of his style which he slowly brought together through the discipline of tempera and of what he calls his "dry-brush watercolors."

He had his first exhibition at the Art Alliance in Philadelphia at age nineteen. The Philadelphia painters Ford Hunter and Yarnall Abbott were members of the committee on exhibits who opened the door. Then Robert Macbeth gave him his first one-man exhibit of watercolors in New York in October, 1937. Andrew Wyeth was twenty years old.

CATALOGUE

Works reproduced in this catalog are indicated thus •

1 CALM MORNING 1938

Martinsville, Maine

Watercolor   20½ x 29½ inches
Lent by Mrs. Paul E. Shorb, Washington, D.C.

2 THE OSPREY 1939

Port Clyde, Maine

Watercolor   21 x 29 inches
Lent by Mr. and Mrs. J. Welles Henderson, Gladwyne, Pa.

• **3 THE COOT HUNTER 1941**

Blubber Butt Island adjoining Teel's Island

Watercolor   17¾ x 29¹³⁄₁₆ inches   Signed at lower right
Lent by The Art Institute of Chicago, The Olivia Shaler Swan Memorial Collection

4 THE HILL 1942

Study for *Winter Fields* (No.5). Painted on the high ground above Kuerner's farm. At first Wyeth made very complete preliminary studies for his pictures in tempera, carrying the drawings almost as far as the completed pictures.

Dry brush and ink drawing   17¼ x 38½ inches   Signed at lower right
Lent by Mr. and Mrs. Samuel F. B. Morse, Pebble Beach, Calif.

5 WINTER FIELDS 1942

These are the fields above Kuerner's. Rebelling against impressionism of style which was leading him, he felt, away from nature into effects only of paint, Wyeth now began a conscious effort to capture what he calls "the truth of the object." The texture of a piece of grass, the feathers of a bird, the little flowers which children called fairy lanterns, seemed wonderful to him; he wanted to bring their qualities into his painting. He began this effort quite in isolation and was surprised, when the picture was shown in the exhibit of *Magic Realism* at the Museum of Modern Art (1943), to learn that other artists were moving in the same direction. The calligraphy of his early pen drawings carried over into the swift, elegant, decorative brush stroke of these early temperas.

Tempera   17¼ x 41 inches
Lent by Mr. Benno Schmidt, New York (Baltimore, New York and Chicago)

13

● **6** PUBLIC SALE 1943

One cold winter day Wyeth and his wife, Betsy, went with a friend, Bert Guest, an antique dealer, to a country auction in the Conestoga valley. The farmer, a tall, lanky Pennsylvanian, whose wife had died three or four months before, took them through the house whose contents were being sold. The loneliness and sadness of a man forced to sell all the objects he had lived with impressed Wyeth. He painted this picture afterward to express the mood of that day. It is one of the few pictures Wyeth painted entirely from memory without any studies on the spot. In spite of this, it shows him drawing closer to nature, adopting a more natural, less obviously designed style, although its structure is much more decorative than in his later work.

Tempera   22 x 48 inches   Signed at lower right
Lent by Mrs. Henry W. Breyer, Jr., Bryn Mawr, Pa.

7 BLACKBERRY PICKERS 1943

Painted on the hill just above Adam Johnson's house one summer when the artist was in Pennsylvania. In deep summer the countryside at Chadds Ford becomes a green jungle, the darkness of its foliage intensified by the heavy mist of heat hanging over it. The key to the picture was set by the glint of the shiny berries.

Tempera   28¾ x 47¾ inches   Signed at lower right
Lent by Mr. Stephen Currier, Farquier County, Va.

• 8 MUDDY ROAD BY ADAM JOHNSON'S 1943

Adam Johnson's house on the left

Ink wash   17 x 21⅜ inches   Signed at lower right
Lent by Mrs. Andrew Wyeth

9 CROWS 1944

Study for *Woodshed*. The crows are hanging on the door of Kuerner's woodshed.

Dry brush and ink drawing   33 x 47 inches   Signed at lower right
Lent by Lyman Allyn Museum, New London, Conn.

10 FRONT DOOR 1944

This is the Kelleran house (near the one general store) in the tiny village of Cushing. The unused front door, freshly painted, in good repair, facing the long grass and the spruce woods (in the country, people always used the kitchen door) said something to him about New England which he wished to record.

Tempera   22 x 33 inches   Signed at lower left
Lent by Mr. Roger S. Firestone, Bryn Mawr, Pa. (Philadelphia)

11 YOUNG FISHERMAN AND DORY 1944

This is a preliminary study for a tempera called *To the Westward*. Realizing, as he put it, that "I was skimming along on a very superficial level, I had a terrible urge to get deeper, closer to nature", he made this very careful study directly from nature. Later he found that such full-sized preparations were no longer needed and seemed to dull the freshness of the finished work. At this time, however, they were a necessary discipline. The study is, in fact, rather more advanced in style than the tempera. It was painted on Teel's Island, Maine.

Dry brush   20⅞ x 33⅞ inches   Signed at lower right
Lent by William A. Farnsworth Library and Art Museum, Rockland, Me.

12 CORN SHOCKS 1945

Fields above Kuerner's

Dry brush   14¼ x 28¾ inches   Signed at lower right
Lent by Mr. and Mrs. Oscar B. Huffman, Santa Fe, N. Mex.

- **13 PULP WOODSMAN 1945**

Hoffses House, Waldboro, Maine

Watercolor   21 x 29 inches   Signed at lower left
Lent anonymously

14 MOTHER ARCHIE'S CHURCH 1945

Scattered through the countryside near Chadds Ford are a number of small octagonal stone schoolhouses. Built by the Quakers in this form, it is said, so that the sun would light the interior at all times of day, they are now for the most part abandoned or turned to other uses. The one nearest Wyeth's home had been taken over by a Negro congregation led by a preacher called Mother Archie. In 1945 it was already abandoned and now it is gone. One day in very early spring Wyeth went into the empty building. A storm had just passed over. The sun gleamed on the brilliant green of winter wheat outside. Inside there was no sound but the cooing of pigeons. The walls still seemed filled with the half darkness of the storm. This was the moment in the life of the decaying building he wished to paint.

Tempera   25 x 48 inches
Lent by Addison Gallery of American Art, Phillips Academy, Andover, Mass.

- **15 YOUNG BUCK 1945**

Kuerner's Barn

Watercolor   29 x 22¾ inches   Signed at lower right
Lent by Mr. and Mrs. W. Glasgow Reynolds, Greenville, Del.

III. *THE SECOND PHASE*

The country road runs down past Mother Archie's Church, passes Kuerner's Farm and goes over a railroad track that was once an important line but is today used by only one freight train a day. The artist's father, N. C. Wyeth, illustrator, painter and muralist, was killed in an automobile accident at that crossing in 1945. He was a man of extraordinary vitality and magnetism whose death was a great shock to all who knew him. It marks an epoch in the development of Andrew Wyeth, not so much in his style as in his inner development. It sharpened all his perceptions, and deepened the web of memories which attached themselves to every part of this little valley where, when the children were small, their father used to take them walking on Sundays. From this time his paintings became more austere, less obviously designed; painting became for him a clear, objective vehicle of expression rather than a display of art.

● **16 BECKIE KING 1946**

Painted at Chadds Ford

Pencil drawing   28½ x 34 inches
Lent by Dallas Museum of Fine Arts, gift of Mr. E. de Golyer

17 WINTER MORNING 1946

The side of Kuerner's barn

Dry brush drawing   25 x 37½ inches   Signed at lower left
Lent by Mr. Loring W. Coleman, Sudbury, Mass.

18 KUERNER'S HILL 1946

Study for *Winter 1946*

Dry brush watercolor   22 x 44 inches   Inscribed at the lower right: *to Joseph Hergesheimer/with deepest regards/Andy Wyeth*
Lent by Mr. and Mrs. R. L. B. Tobin, San Antonio, Tex.

• **19 WINTER 1946**

This was the first tempera done after his father's death. One winter day, while walking, he saw a neighbor's boy dressed in an old World War II uniform running down Kuerner's hill. The power and bigness of the hill, and the running, almost tumbling figure of the boy, seemed to say something about the enduring Pennsylvania countryside he loved, about his father and his own loss: it is a picture filled with overtones. The picture began as a large view of the hill, on which the boy's figure was tiny in the distance, as Wyeth actually saw him. A dry-brush watercolor, *Kuerner's Hill*, which precedes, shows this stage of the idea.

Tempera   38 x 56 inches   Signed at lower right
Lent by Mr. and Mrs. John D. MacDonald, Cambridge, Mass.
(Philadelphia, Baltimore and New York)

• **20 FOUR POSTER 1946**

A study in dry brush watercolor for Arthur Cleveland (No.21). Even larger than the tempera for which it is a preparation, it is an example of the exact, disciplined observation in which Wyeth was now training himself. Painted in Lafayette's headquarters, Chadds Ford. The memory of the farmer in the Conestoga valley who had shown them through his house (see *Public Sale*, No.6) had lingered in Wyeth's memory. He returned to the theme of the solitary man and the emptied house in this picture and the tempera that follows.

Dry brush   40 x 29½ inches
Lent by Mr. and Mrs. Roger Milliken, Spartanburg, S.C.

21 ARTHUR CLEVELAND 1946

Arthur Cleveland was a man of good Philadelphia family, educated, traveled, who settled into a country life in Chadds Ford. He and his wife bought the old stone house, built about 1710, which had been Lafayette's headquarters before the battle of Brandywine, and raised a family there. His tall, powerful figure within the low-ceilinged room, beside the old four-poster bed, seemed to Wyeth a symbol of the strength and continuity of the Pennsylvania countryside. It is characteristic that when Wyeth painted a figure, it was that of someone he had known all his life.

Tempera   42 x 30¾ inches   Signed at upper left
Lent by The Wilmington Society of the Fine Arts, Wilmington, Del.

22 CRYSTAL LAMP 1946

Living room of Betsy Wyeth's parent's home in Cushing

Watercolor   29 x 21 inches   Signed at lower left
Lent by Hotel du Pont, Wilmington, Del.

23 HOFFMAN'S SLOUGH 1947

This view looks across the valley of the Brandywine and the still water where Wyeth used to skate in winter as a child. It was also a place filled with memories of his father. The sun is going down; the shadow of the western hills creeping across the valley "is like the eyelid of night closing," as he said. This view of the subject is unrecognizable by the casual visitor, however, for the artist has stripped the valley bare of its trees, houses, paved road, fences, telephone poles, of everything except the one tiny stone house of John Chadd. It is the valley seen by the inner eye of the mind.

Tempera   41 x 54½ inches   Signed at lower right
Lent by Mrs. Charles B. Mayer, New York

24 CHRISTINA OLSON 1947

This is the first of three pictures of Christina Olson, who with her brother is a neighbor of the Wyeths in Maine. He saw her one day sitting in the late afternoon sun looking at the sea. The sun and shadow struck slanting across the weathered Maine door. "Wood weathers differently there by the sea" and Wyeth is pleased that he caught the worn quality of the wood. He was to return to the subject of the human being many times.

Tempera   33 x 25 inches   Signed at lower left
Lent by Mr. and Mrs. Joseph Verner Reed, New York

• 25 WIND FROM THE SEA 1947

Painted in one of the upper rooms of the Olson house, which Wyeth was using as a studio. He went up there one day; the room was dry and hot and he threw up the window to cool the room. After beginning the picture, he had to wait two months for another wind from the west to study the blowing curtains. "You can't make these things up," he said. "You must see how it was. Everything was dry and hot—the shade curtains, the lace, the window frame. I tried to get that quality, and the air blowing."

Tempera   18½ x 27½ inches   Signed at upper right
Lent by Professor and Mrs. Charles H. Morgan, Amherst, Mass.

26 KARL 1948

Karl Kuerner was in the German army in the 1914 war, migrated to America, rented a house from Arthur Cleveland, bought it, prospered and is now a solid citizen of Chadds Ford. He retains from the Old World some ways of the old-fashioned self-sufficient farmer, as well as a great respect for artists. He, his house, his fields and animals, have played a great role in Wyeth's work. This was the first portrait after the death of N. C. Wyeth. Although Karl Kuerner is a farmer and N. C. Wyeth was an artist, Andrew Wyeth saw something of his father's strength in the face he painted here. Painted at Kuerner's house.

Tempera   30⅝ x 23⅝ inches   Signed at lower right
Lent by Private Collection, New York (Philadelphia and New York)

• **27 CHRISTINA OLSON 1948**

Study for *Christina's World*. About this time, finding that very careful preparatory studies in color were no longer necessary and that they cooled his feeling in the finished work, Wyeth changed to a briefer, though still exact notation in pencil. Drawn from life at Olsons'.

Pencil drawing $14\frac{7}{16}$ x $20\frac{1}{2}$ inches   Signed at lower right
Lent by Mrs. Andrew Wyeth

• **28 CHRISTINA'S WORLD 1948**

The Olson family, brother and sister, live on a farm near the Wyeths in Maine. The brother, once a fisherman, has turned truck gardener; his sister, though partly crippled by infantile paralysis, keeps house for him. Their house, their life have become symbols of great importance to Wyeth and have furnished him many subjects. None, perhaps, has made a deeper impression than this picture. Alvaro, the brother, does not like to pose. There is only one early picture of him, *Oil Lamp*, in Houston. Christina is, to Wyeth, a remarkable woman. She has a keen mind and is interested in nature, although so crippled that she moves about by crawling or moving in a chair. This picture grew out of a very slight incident—simply the sight of her out picking berries near the family burying ground, looking back across the field toward her house where Wyeth was working in an upper room. Christina moves with such difficulty that this, as the title says, is her world. Painted at the Olson farm.

Tempera $32\frac{1}{4}$ x $47\frac{3}{4}$ inches   Signed at lower right
Lent by The Museum of Modern Art, New York (New York)

29 SEED CORN 1948

This was painted in the attic of the Olson house in Maine. Seed corn, saved for the next year and hung in the attic, seemed typical of New England ways; it speaks, in Wyeth's mind, of every farm in Maine. His choice of the subject illustrates a tendency which was to grow steadily stronger in his art, to make a small fragment of the world, vividly stated, imply the unseen whole of which it is part.

Tempera   14 x 22 inches   Signed at lower right
Lent by Mr. and Mrs. John D. MacDonald, Cambridge, Mass.
(Philadelphia, Baltimore and New York)

30 WINTER CORN 1948

Done in the field above Lafayette's headquarters, Chadds Ford

Dry brush drawing   29 x 39 inches   Signed at lower right
Lent anonymously

31 MARGARET HANDY 1949

Preparatory study for the tempera (No.32) Drawn in artist's studio

Pencil drawing   9 x 10½ inches
Lent by Mrs. Andrew Wyeth

• **32 CHILDREN'S DOCTOR 1949**

Painted at artist's Chadds Ford studio

Margaret Handy, to the horror of her conservative Baltimore mother, chose a career in medicine and was one of the first women to graduate from Johns Hopkins Medical School. She took care of the Wyeth boys and many other children of their acquaintance, and is an old and dear friend of the family. It is characteristic of Wyeth to paint a portrait which is not a portrait: it is an expression of affection and a vivid memory.

Tempera   26 x 25 inches   Signed at lower right
Lent by Dr. Margaret I. Handy, Chadds Ford, Pa.

33 SPRING EVENING 1949

Painted in house next to Archie's church below Adam Johnson's

Dry brush   22¼ x 28½ inches   Signed at upper right
Lent by Mrs. Stephen Etnier, South Harpswell, Me.

34 THE REVENANT 1949

A self-portrait of an unusual sort painted in the Olson house. Wyeth had been out sailing. Coming in with his eyes full of sun and sea, he was startled by the apparition of himself in a dusty mirror in an unused room. That is the picture.

Tempera   30 x 20 inches
Lent by New Britain Museum of American Art, New Britain, Conn.

● **35 YOUNG AMERICA 1950**

This is the same Chadds Ford boy who is running down the hill in *Winter 1946* (No.19). For a time he looked after the two Wyeth boys and practically lived in the Wyeth house. He decorated their station wagon, like his bicycle, with foxtails and rode about, as Wyeth puts it, like a mixture of young boy and General Custer. Open country around Chadds Ford.

Tempera   32½ x 46 inches   Signed at lower left
Lent by Pennsylvania Academy of the Fine Arts, Philadelphia

36 NIGHT LAMP 1950

This is the same Quaker schoolhouse that appears in *Mother Archie's Church* (No.14). In 1950 a Negro family was living in it. One fresh, dark, moist spring night, Wyeth passing by and seeing the light coming out in all directions from the windows, thought: The whole building is turned into a lamp. That is the picture.

Tempera   14¼ x 20 inches   Signed at lower right
Lent by Mrs. Josiah Marvel, Greenville, Del. (Philadelphia and New York)

37 BELOW DOVER 1950

The model for this was a Friendship sloop in Maine but the experience out of which it grew was the memory of a Chesapeake Bay sharpie pulled up on the Delaware shore in the marshes below Dover. It was painted from imagination, in Cushing, Maine studio.

Tempera   10 x 16 inches   Signed at lower left
Lent by Mrs. Andrew Wyeth

38 HENRY'S DORY 1950

Study for Spindrift (No.39) Teel's Island, Me.

Dry brush drawing   8¾ x 21¾ inches
Lent by Mr. Gordon M. Smith, Buffalo, N.Y.

39 SPINDRIFT 1950

Henry Teel would come in from hauling lobster pots about ten-thirty in the morning, pull his dory up on the beach, stow his oars and tackle neatly, and go indoors to cook himself a meal. This is a portrait of Henry without showing the man himself: these are all the things he used, shaped by life and by the sea.

Tempera   15 x 36 inches   Signed at lower left
Lent by The Currier Gallery of Art, Manchester, N.H.

40 LIGHTNING ROD 1950

One of the many pencil and watercolor studies made in preparation for the tempera that follows. Drawn on Teel's Island.

Pencil drawing 19 x 14½ inches   Inscribed at the lower right: *Sky and water quite down in key/small glint on lightning rod globe brightest/spot/roof down keep in key/A.W.*

Lent by Mr. and Mrs. Philip Hofer, Houghton Library, Harvard University

● **41 NORTHERN POINT 1950**

One summer morning in 1950 Wyeth climbed out on the weathered roof of Henry Teel's house to see the sea and islands beyond. The fog was burning off, but the horizon was still hidden; the sun just coming through gleamed on the water and on the amber ball of the lightning rod. The sharp, black point and shining ball against the pale light brought back memories of the sensation of climbing on a roof as a child, and became a symbol of that strange aerial excitement. When Henry Teel came back in midmorning from pulling his lobster pots, he looked up at the figure on his roof and grumbled, "Where'r my guinea hens goin' to roost tonight?" then went indoors and presently the acrid smell of a driftwood fire in the wood stove and of coffee mingled with the rime in the air.

Tempera   36 x 18³⁄₁₆ inches   Signed at lower left
Lent by Wadsworth Atheneum,
The Ella Gallup Sumner and Mary Catlin Sumner Collection, Hartford, Conn.

• 42 TOP VIEW OF TURKEY BUZZARD 1950

Study for Soaring (No.44) Looking down on fields above Adam Johnson's

Pencil drawing   13 x 20 inches   Inscribed at lower center: *Top view of Turkey Buzzard drawing from life. A.W.*
Lent by Museum of Fine Arts of Boston, bequest of Maxim Karolik

43 TURKEY BUZZARD 1950

Study for Soaring (No.44)

Pencil   16¾ x 26 inches   Inscribed center: *Turkey Buzzard study from life*
Lent by Museum of Fine Arts of Boston

• 44 SOARING 1950

This picture had many adventures on the road to completion. It was begun very early, not long after *Winter Fields* (No.5). Wyeth likes to watch the turkey vultures which are a feature of the Chester County sky, and wondering how the countryside, where he had lived all his life, looked to the soaring bird, began this picture. His father showed no interest in it and Wyeth laid it aside unfinished. Presently the big panel was serving as a table for Nicky's toy railroad. Some years later, Lincoln Kirstein saw and liked it and encouraged Wyeth to finish it. It is done looking down on fields near Adam Johnson's.

Tempera   48 x 87 inches   Signed at lower right
Lent by Shelburne Museum, Shelburne, Vt. (Philadelphia, Baltimore and New York)

45 THE TRODDEN WEED 1951

Wyeth inherited from his father a love of historical costume. During his recovery from a long illness in the winter of 1950-51, his wife gave him a pair of horseman's boots, which had once belonged to Howard Pyle and then to Stanley Arthur. Struggling to regain his strength, Wyeth began to take walks. He was not strong enough to carry his watercolor equipment so he just walked and walked; finding the boots fitted him comfortably, he wore them. Constantly watching his feet, owing to his slow pace, he thought of this picture, which came to symbolize the relation between his critical illness and refusal to accept it—"a kind of stalking away." "The execution of the tempera was painfully slow. I had to work at first with my arm resting in a sling suspended from the ceiling."

Tempera   20 x 18¼ inches   Signed at lower right
Lent by Mrs. Andrew Wyeth

Sternum of Turkey Buzzard
drawn from life
ALE

44 SOARING 1950

● **46 BOOTS 1951**

Preparatory study for *The Trodden Weed* (No.45)

Pencil drawing   10¼ x 13¼ inches   Signed at lower right
Lent by Mrs. Andrew Wyeth

47 HIS BOOT 1951

Walking one day along the shore of **Teel's Island,** Wyeth came on one of Henry
Teel's boots. Henry himself was then living on the mainland. The sight of this
worn, familiar part of his life, left behind, symbolized the haunted feeling of
the empty island.

Dry brush   15½ x 19½ inches   Signed at lower left
Lent by Mr. and Mrs. Robert W. Stoddard, Worcester, Mass.

● **48 MAN FROM MAINE 1951**

A momentary pose of a friend, Forrest Wall, looking out of the window in the
artist's house at Cushing seemed to symbolize the curiosity of the New Englander
—"Who's that going by?" "Stay just as you are," Wyeth said. The friend
stood there for three weeks. "I'll never look out of a window again," was his
comment.

Tempera   20½ x 20 inches   Signed at lower left
Lent by Mrs. Stephen Etnier, South Harpswell, Me.

49 TOLL ROPE 1951

In these days of automobiles and paved roads, the small country churches of Maine are often used only for funerals. Wyeth remembers them as always dry and echoing, unused. Halfway up the rickety ladder to the belfry, in one, there was a wooden anchor wrapped in crepe: he still remembers the color of the faded crepe. Years later, in another church, he painted this—at Wylie's corner, St. George, Maine.

Tempera   28½ x 11 inches   Signed at lower right
Lent by Mr. and Mrs. William A. Worth, Greenville, Del.

50 SHAG FROM GEORGE'S RIVER 1951

Drawn from life

Pencil drawing   17 x 23 inches   Signed at lower right
Lent by Mrs. Andrew Wyeth

51 JAMES LOPER 1952

James Loper was a big man, strong bodied, but simple-minded; he died insane. Wyeth had known him from childhood, had gone to school with him, and accepted him, as people do in a village, as a natural part of life. But beyond that, the artist has (as this exhibit shows) a wonderful sympathy and interest in human beings so simple that their lives, passed instinctively, hardly emerge into the self-conscious world of intellect and will in which the successful in life dwell. He saw James Loper once leaning against Ben Loper's chicken coop. Ben Loper (*A Crow Flew By* in the Metropolitan Museum of Art) and his wife took care of James and he called them his parents, although they were not. The evening light struck the wall behind and a big scythe hung overhead. Wyeth painted James as he had accepted him.

Tempera   21 x 43½ inches   Signed at lower right
Lent by Mr. and Mrs. Harry G. Haskell, Jr., Wilmington, Del.

● **52 FARAWAY 1952**

Wyeth considers this one of the first really successful pictures in his dry brush technique. He had been out walking with his son Jamie. The boy lost a lead soldier and turning, Wyeth walked back down the hill to look for it. After a vain search, he looked for Jamie. The boy had already given up the search and was sitting on the dry grass, lost in dreams. He was wearing a "Davy Crockett" fur hat that had been given him for Christmas and metal-tipped shoes, which he was proud of because they had been worn by some boy before the Civil War.

Dry brush   13½ x 21 inches   Signed at lower right
Lent by Mrs. Andrew Wyeth

43

53 CHICKEN WIRE 1952

Ben Loper farm, Chadds Ford

Pencil drawing   19 x 25 inches   Signed at lower right
Lent by Mr. and Mrs. Courtland D. Barnes, New York (Baltimore and New York)

54 CHARRED BUTTONWOOD 1952

Preparatory study for *April Wind* (No.55)

Dry brush   10 x 19½ inches   Signed at lower right
Lent by Mr. and Mrs. Nelson R. Kandel, Baltimore, Md.

55 APRIL WIND 1952

This is another picture of James Loper, painted on the hill on Kuerner's farm. The artist once saw the big man, who became strange when the moon was full, sitting like this with the wind blowing his long coat. The still figure speaks.

Tempera   20 x 26 inches   Signed at lower right
Lent by Wadsworth Atheneum, Hartford, Conn.

• **56 MISS OLSON 1952**

When the artist returned for the third time to the subject of Christina Olson, painting her holding a sick kitten, he simplified the picture until it is the face alone that counts. "I am better," he said, "when I work with fewer objects. But I have to start with a rich concept and boil it down to its essence." The three pictures (Nos.24,27;28) show his development in making the small detail imply the larger whole of which it is a part. Painted at the Olson farm.

Tempera   25 x 28½ inches   Signed at lower right
Lent by Private Collection, New York (Philadelphia and New York)

57 MILK PAILS 1953

Wylie farm, Chadds Ford

Preparatory study for *Cooling Shed* (No.58)

Pencil drawing   5¼ x 5¾ inches
Lent by Mrs. Andrew Wyeth

● **58 COOLING SHED 1953**

The milk sheds of the Wylies' farm are cooled by a spring that has been bubbling there since pre-Revolutionary days; the boards have been whitewashed so many times that they are thick and peeling. Wyeth used to walk to the Wylie farm and often had lunches with the family. One autumn day when the afternoon sun streamed in reflecting along the white walls, striking the milk pails and the golden piece of chamois, Wyeth found his subject. In the artist's mind this cool passage implies a kind of day in the whole valley.

Tempera   24¾ x 12½ inches   Signed at lower left
Lent by Mrs. Josiah Marvel, Greenville, Del. (Philadelphia and New York)

59 OUT OF SEASON 1953

Hill on the Kuerner farm

Dry brush   13¼ x 20½ inches   Signed at lower right
Lent by Mr. and Mrs. John Warner, 3rd, Clinton, Ill.

60 TARPAULIN 1953

Adam Johnson's farm above Archie's Church

Watercolor   19½ x 27½ inches   Signed at lower left
Lent by Mr. W. S. Carpenter, Jr., Wilmington, Del.

61 THE CORNER 1953

Mother Archie's Church here appears again. Though usually called a dry brush, this is predominately true watercolor and was painted in a single morning. The dry brush technique was used only for some details in the distance.

Watercolor and dry brush   13½ x 21½ inches   Signed at lower right
Lent by The Wilmington Society of the Fine Arts, The Phelps Collection,
Wilmington, Del.

62 FLOCK OF CROWS 1953

Hill on the Kuerner Farm

Preparatory study for *Snow Flurries* (No.64)

Dry brush drawing   9½ x 19 inches   Signed at lower right
Lent by Mrs. Andrew Wyeth

63 ARCHIE'S CORNER 1953

Across the road from Archie's Church

Preparatory study for *Snow Flurries* (No.64)

Pencil drawing   13 x 18 inches   Signed at lower right
Lent by Dr. Margaret I. Handy, Chadds Ford, Pa.

64 SNOW FLURRIES 1953

The artist has spent most of his life walking on this hill on the Kuerner Farm facing Ring Road, so he decided to do a portrait of it. *Hoffman's Slough* (No.23) is a mental image. This, while simplified—the ruin seen in *Archie's Corner* is omitted, for instance—is much more nearly a portrait and was carefully studied from nature in many drawings.

Tempera   36 x 47 inches
Lent by Dr. Margaret I. Handy, Chadds Ford, Pa.

65 BUCKET POST 1953

On the Adam Johnson Farm

Watercolor $22\frac{1}{2}$ x 29 inches   Signed at lower left
Lent by W. B. Connor Foundation, Danbury, Conn.

66 SEA SHELLS 1953

Preparatory study for *Sandspit* (No.67), painted on the East side of Georges River across from the Wyeth's home in Cushing.

Dry brush drawing $11\frac{5}{16}$ x $15\frac{5}{16}$ inches   Signed at lower right
Lent by Mrs. Andrew Wyeth

• **67 SANDSPIT 1953**

The artist's wife looking at birds on a clear, bright Maine morning. The artist was fascinated by the multiplicity of shells in the sandspit and wished to suggest the countless number of things of which it is composed, while keeping the large simplicity of the whole shape.

Tempera $35\frac{1}{2}$ x 48 inches   Signed at lower right
Lent anonymously

68 CREEK BED 1953

Brinton's Run, Chadds Ford

Pencil drawing $13\frac{5}{8}$ x 20 inches
Lent by Mrs. Andrew Wyeth

69 UNDER WATER 1953

Brinton's Run, Chadds Ford

Pencil drawing $13\frac{1}{2}$ x $21\frac{1}{2}$ inches
Lent by Mrs. Andrew Wyeth

49

70 BIRD WATCHER 1953

Broad Cove Farm, Wyeth's home in Cushing

Watercolor   20 x 28 inches
Lent by Mr. and Mrs. Edward Gerry, Westbury, N. Y.

71 KARL'S ROOM 1954

Karl's bedroom on the Kuerner Farm

Watercolor   21½ x 29¾ inches   Signed at lower right
Lent by Museum of Fine Arts, Houston,
gift of Mrs. W. S. Farish (Philadelphia)

72 KITCHEN ELL 1954

The ell of Henry Teel's house

Dry brush drawing   14 x 18 inches
Lent by Mrs. Andrew Wyeth

73 LIFEBOAT HOUSE 1954

Marshall Point Light, Port Clyde, Maine

Watercolor   21 x 29 inches   Signed at lower right
Lent by Mr. and Mrs. Charles Brisk, New York

74 MARSH GRASS 1954

The Teel house on Teel's Island

Watercolor   19 x 27½ inches   Signed at lower left
Lent anonymously

75 CORNER OF THE WOODS 1954

Betsy Wyeth sitting under a beech tree, looking at birds, was again the model, although the likeness is not close. The quality of a person lost in thought, the color of the beech trunk and of beech leaves faded by winter storms, are the real subjects. Painted on a path leading to Adam Johnson's.

Tempera 38½ x 30½ inches Signed at lower right
Lent by Mr. William A. Coolidge, Cambridge, Mass.

76 TOMORROW THE OUTER SHOALS 1954

These white, newly painted lobster buoys hanging in the darkness, like ghosts in a dark room, make an interesting composition. It is questionable if Wyeth would have painted them, however, if they had not belonged to Betsy's brother-in-law who, after a career in business in New York City, and service with the Navy in the South Seas, returned to manage the family lobster fishing business in Maine. In other words, these too belong to Wyeth's own life and form part of his inner experience. Painted in Sherwood Cook's fishhouse, Martinsville, Maine.

Tempera 19½ x 36¼ inches Signed at upper left
Lent anonymously (Philadelphia and Baltimore)

● 77 TEEL'S ISLAND 1954

Henry Teel's house, in the distance, was built from the timbers of a British man-of-war wrecked on the island during the Revolution. A Crown musket from the wreck was preserved in the house. The lightning rod seen in *Northern Point* (No.41) stands out against the sky. Henry Teel's boat was normally tied up at the wharf or the boat mooring. His last chore before leaving for the mainland in autumn was to haul it up above high water. In 1954 Henry was ill and Wyeth realized, when autumn came around again, that he would probably never use the boat again. So on a crisp bright day near the close of autumn he painted this record of what was past.

Dry brush 10 x 23 inches Signed at lower left
Lent by Mr. and Mrs. Robert Montgomery, New York

● 78 ALEXANDER CHANDLER 1955

The daughter with whom Alexander Chandler lived, would put her blind father out in the morning and he would move around the house with the sun. He kept watch over his grandchildren as they played outdoors. If the voice of one seemed too far distant, he would swing his cane against the wall of the house with a report like a pistol shot and all the grandchildren would come to attention. The old blind grandfather was still a figure of authority, and as he sat looking up with amber-colored eyes at the sun which he could not see, he appealed to Wyeth's love of age and character. Painted in Dilworthtown, Pa.

Dry brush 21½ x 15 inches Signed at lower right
Lent by Mr. and Mrs. Robert Montgomery, New York

79 EDGE OF THE FIELD 1955

Above John Chadd's house, Chadds Ford

Watercolor   19½ x 26½ inches   Signed at lower right
Lent by Colby College Art Museum, Waterville, Me.

80 BENJAMIN'S HOUSE 1955

Ben Loper's, Chadds Ford

Watercolor   21 x 29½ inches   Signed at lower left
Lent by California Palace of the Legion of Honor,
gift of Mrs. Alexander de Bretteville, San Francisco

● **81 NICHOLAS 1955**

The artist's son Nicholas has always taken a deep interest in his father's work.
As a boy he would stop in the studio, as he came home from school, to see what
his father was doing. One day Wyeth noticed him sitting quietly in the studio,
dreaming of his airplanes. Wanting to catch this moment of a child's life, he
painted the picture of Nicholas on a panel upon which there was already a landscape, so that the picture of a fleeting moment covers one of an enduring hill.

Tempera   32½ x 30¾ inches
Lent by Mrs. Andrew Wyeth

82 BENNY'S SCARECROW 1955

In the field behind Ben Loper's house

Watercolor   20 x 23¾ inches   Signed at lower right
Lent by Mr. and Mrs. T. Edward Hanley, Bradford, Pa.

83 BLEACHED CRAB 1955

Teel's Island

Watercolor   13⅝ x 25⅝ inches   Signed at lower right
Lent by Mr. James H. Worth, New York

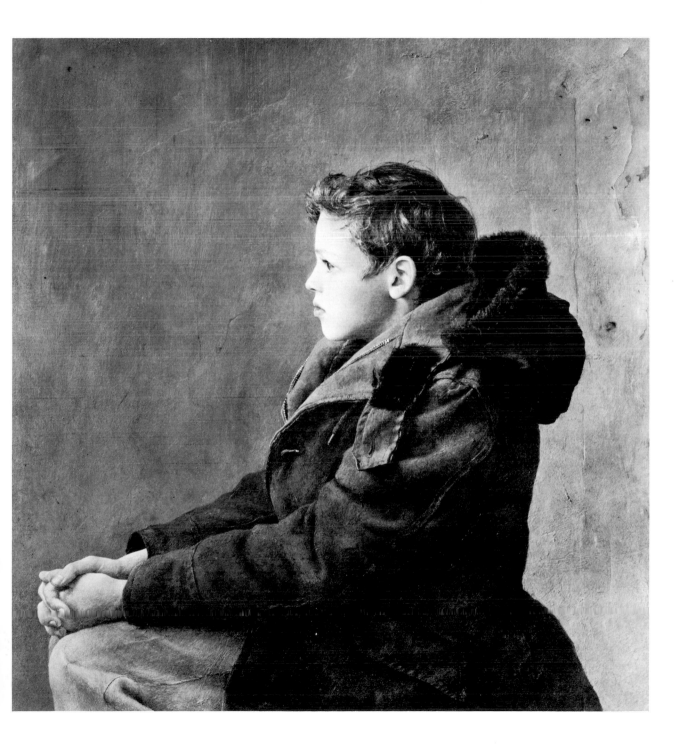

● **84 DELPHINIUM 1955**

In the garden of the artist's mother-in-law at Cushing, Maine

Watercolor   21 x 30 inches   Signed at lower right
Lent by Mr. and Mrs. B. Brewster Jennings, Glen Head, L.I.

85 MEETING HOUSE 1955

South Cushing, Maine

Watercolor   20 x 30 inches   Signed at lower right
Lent by Mr. and Mrs. Kenneth Morse Kurson, Waban, Mass.

86 SOUTH CUSHING 1955

This is a neighbor's horse. Wyeth has not often done horses. With his feeling for
what is characteristic or typical, Wyeth saw the animal, standing in a field still
wearing harness and blinders, as another phase of the life in South Cushing and
therefore interesting to paint.

Tempera   27 x 36¼ inches   Signed at lower right
Lent by Mr. and Mrs. Richard S. West, Beverly, Mass. (Philadelphia)

87 HOGSHEAD 1955

The Olson Barn, South Cushing

Watercolor   20 x 27 inches   Signed at lower left
Lent by Dr. Catherine Bacon, Merion Station, Pa.

88 LET IN THE AIR 1955

The Teel House, Teel's Island

Watercolor   27½ x 19½ inches   Signed at lower right
Lent anonymously

89 BLUE COAT 1955

Painted in artist's studio, Chadds Ford

Watercolor drawing   13⅜ x 10½ inches   Signed at lower right
Lent by Mrs. Andrew Wyeth

90 STUDY OF CORN 1955

Above John Chadd's house

Pencil drawing   13½ x 20½ inches
Lent by Mrs. Andrew Wyeth

91 THE HANDS 1955

Mrs. Winfield's house, Chadds Ford

Pencil drawing   6¾ x 9¾ inches   Signed at lower right
Lent by Mr. and Mrs. Lloyd Goodrich, New York

92 CIDER AND PORK 1955

Karl Kuerner's spring house

Watercolor   21 x 28½ inches   Signed at lower left
Lent by Amanda K. Berls, New York

93 ALLAN 1955

Preparatory study for *Roasted Chestnuts* (No.94)

Dry brush drawing   5 x 5 inches   Signed at lower left
Lent by Mrs. Andrew Wyeth

94 ROASTED CHESTNUTS 1956

One November afternoon, driving to West Chester, Wyeth saw a neighbor boy,
Allan Messersmith, standing by the roadside selling chestnuts. All his life Wyeth
has seen boys by the side of country roads selling chestnuts; the smell of roasted
chestnuts is a part of his memories of winter evenings. This time, the tall thin
figure standing beside his homemade roaster, the late light through gaps in the
Osage orange hedge picking out the ruts by the road's edge, crystallized a host
of such impressions. He made many studies of the boy in his knit cap and old
army jacket, of the oil drum, even of the bare branches of Osage orange, in
preparation for the tempera.

Tempera   48 x 33 inches   Signed at lower left
Lent by Mr. and Mrs. Harry G. Haskell, Jr., Wilmington, Del.

95 ORCHARD RUN 1956

Above the N. C. Wyeth orchard

Watercolor   20 x 28 inches   Signed at lower right
Lent by Mr. and Mrs. George Greenspan, New York (Philadelphia, Baltimore and
New York)

• 96 GRANDDAUGHTER 1956

Grandfather is the same Alexander Chandler who appears in No.78; the granddaughter appears again in *Day of the Fair* (No.195). This grandchild would go up and wake him when he was dozing, to ask him questions. Something of the arrogance of youth toward old age struck Wyeth in the two and he painted this study of their relationship. Dilworthtown, Pa.

Dry brush   16½ x 23½ inches   Signed at lower right
Lent by Mr. and Mrs. Robert Montgomery, New York

97 EGG SCALE 1956

On many Sunday mornings Wyeth has watched Alvaro Olson bring out his egg scale, collect his eggs, scrape them clean with a knife, weigh them, sort them into boxes. The contrast between the big man and the delicate eggs, as well as the golden color of the egg crates, appealed to him and he made a number of studies for a picture which was never executed.

Dry brush drawing   14¹³⁄₁₆ x 17⅞ inches   Signed at lower right
Lent by Mrs. Andrew Wyeth

● **98 THE BED 1956**

Preparatory study for *Chambered Nautilus* (No.99)

Pencil drawing 13⅜ x 19⅞ inches Signed at lower right
Lent by Mrs. Andrew Wyeth

99 CHAMBERED NAUTILUS 1956

Painted in the summer of 1956 during the last illness of Mrs. Wyeth's mother.
The invalid could look out from her bed into the sunshine on the sea. She kept
a little basket by her bed, to hold her Bible, pencils and the other little things
that were her life. In the late afternoon she would open the door and the wind
from the river would blow the curtains. "I did the picture right there in the
room," the artist said, "and she would talk to me about her childhood in Con-
necticut. She was a great woman, one of those people who never grow old. It was
a very touching experience. I never painted her head close-up and have always
regretted that. But Betsy is very like her and there is a great deal of her in *Maga's
Daughter*" (No.221). Painted in Mrs. Merle James' bedroom, Broad Cove
Farm, Cushing.

Tempera 25 x 48 inches Signed at upper right
Lent by Mr. and Mrs. Robert Montgomery, New York

100 TOM CLARK 1956

Tom Clark's house, Chadds Ford

Dry brush drawing 9½ x 10½ inches Signed at upper left
Lent by Mr. and Mrs. Andrew J. Sordoni, Jr., Forty-Fort, Pa.

101 PETER HURD 1956

The artist's brother-in-law and friend, an artist as devoted to the landscape of
New Mexico as Wyeth is to Pennsylvania and Maine.

Pencil drawing 11 x 8¼ inches
Lent by Mrs. Andrew Wyeth

102 ROPE AND CHAINS 1956

Preparatory study for *Brown Swiss* (No.107)

Pencil drawing 16¾ x 22¾ inches Signed at lower right
Lent by Mrs. Andrew Wyeth

103 CORN CUTTING KNIFE 1956

Painted in artist's studio, Chadds Ford

Watercolor 20 x 14 inches Signed at lower left
Lent by Mr. and Mrs. Robert L. B. Tobin, San Antonio, Tex.

104 FARM POND 1957

Preparatory study for *Brown Swiss* (No.107)

Watercolor   13⅓ x 22 inches   Signed at lower right
Lent by Mrs. Frederick H. Lassiter, New York

105 OIL DRUM 1957

The Kuerner Farm

Dry brush   13½ x 20½ inches   Signed at lower left
Lent by Mr. and Mrs. Henry Loeb, New York

106 CHIMNEY SMOKE 1957

The Kuerner Farm

Watercolor   21½ x 29¾ inches   Signed at lower left
Lent by Mr. and Mrs. Oscar B. Huffman, Santa Fe, N. Mex.

● **107 BROWN SWISS 1957**

The house of Karl Kuerner is a typical Pennsylvania farmhouse of about 1840
with some additions of later date. Wyeth has been in and out of its rooms,
painted its owner, stood near it to paint *The Hill* (No.4) and many other pictures. One November day, as Wyeth was passing, the late afternoon sun struck
its west front and was reflected in the cattle pond. The scene in its fine simplicity
of light and color seemed to him to sum up the Pennsylvania landscape
in winter. He made many studies of details (some of which are shown here), in-
cluding the Brown Swiss cattle in winter pasture around the pond. As he said
once, "however, I keep these drawings around, not to copy, but they give me
warmth when I come to paint." When at last he brought all these together, he
left out the cattle and most of the other details, giving what is essentially a
portrait from memory, heightened by affection, given intensity by the artist's
power of vivid expression.

Tempera   30 x 60⅛ inches   Signed at lower right
Lent by Mr. and Mrs. Alexander M. Laughlin, New York (Philadelphia)

108 CITIZEN CLARK 1957

Tom Clark was born in lower Delaware, one of the people known in that rural locality as Moors. His slanted blue eyes and strong aquiline features are different from those of his Negro neighbors. He was a man of great and austere dignity which interested Wyeth to paint him several times. Tom Clark lived in Chadds Ford. Painted in Tom Clark's house.

Dry brush   14⅜ x 22⅜ inches   Signed at lower left
Lent by Mr. and Mrs. Alexander M. Laughlin, New York (New York)

● **109 HAY LEDGE 1957**

When Alvaro Olson gave up fishing, he stored his dory in his barn which became filled with hay, cobwebs, mowing machines and so on. To the artist, the dory gleaming in the light reflected from the floor up through the timbers of the barn, seemed as if hung up on hay rather than on rocks; so he called the picture *Hay Ledge*. Alvaro Olson Barn.

Tempera   21½ x 45 inches   Signed at lower left
Lent by Mrs. Coleman Woolworth, San Francisco

110 WINDFALLS 1957

In the N. C. Wyeth orchard, Chadds Ford

Watercolor   20 x 28 inches   Signed at lower right
Lent by Mr. and Mrs. James Fosburgh, New York (Philadelphia)

111 ATWATER LAND 1957

Below Adam Johnson's farm

Watercolor   19½ x 28 inches
Lent by Mr. and Mrs. Andrew Sordoni, Jr., Forty-Fort, Pa.

112 BRINTON'S MILL 1957

Preparatory study for *Raccoon* (No.115)

Dry brush   13 x 21¼ inches   Signed at upper left
Lent by Mrs. Andrew Wyeth

113 HOUND 1957

Preparatory study for *Raccoon* (No.115)

Dry brush drawing   14¾ x 22½ inches   Signed at lower left
Lent by Mrs. Andrew Wyeth

114 SLEEPING DOG 1958

Preparatory study for *Raccoon* (No.115)

Watercolor drawing   10 x 12 inches   Signed at lower left
Lent by Mrs. Andrew Wyeth

● **115 RACCOON 1958**

Brinton's Mill, Chadds Ford

When Brinton's Mill, which was to become the Wyeths' home, first appeared in his work, it was occupied by a family of poor whites from South Carolina. The man of the family worked as an automobile mechanic but his real life was hunting. He kept his coon dogs chained and starved in the barn; Wyeth used to feed them when he walked over there. Once he was invited to go on a coon hunt and, although he hates hunting, went along to see what it was like. They went up near Reading, walked all night, lost the dogs for hours. Wyeth fell in a stream in the darkness, was soaked to the waist, and came home at four in the morning without having seen a raccoon. This was his one taste of coon hunting; but since he painted this picture, people think him an enthusiastic hunter.

Tempera   48 x 48 inches   Signed at lower left
Lent by Mr. and Mrs. Harry G. Haskell, Jr., Wilmington, Del.

● **116** FORGET-ME-NOTS 1958

Spring house looking toward Brinton's Mill

Watercolor   20 x 29 inches   Signed at lower left
Lent by Mrs. Madison H. Lewis, New York

117 DRY WELL 1958

Olson House, South Cushing

Watercolor   20 x 29¾ inches   Signed at lower right
Lent by Mrs. Ledyard Cogswell, Loudenville, N.Y.

118 UP RIVER 1958

Georges River above the Wyeth house

Watercolor   18½ x 27½ inches   Signed at lower left
Lent by Mrs. Alfred E. Bissell, Wilmington, Del.

• **119 THE SLIP** 1958

A two-masted Chesapeake Bay "bug-eye", owned at that time by the Coast Guard, spent the summer of 1958 pulled up in a slip in Rockland harbor. The beautiful boat lying there derelict, as the fog rolled in one day half-concealing the sail loft behind, seemed to Wyeth a symbol of Rockland harbor and the past: this was its end.

Dry brush   20 x 29⅛ inches   Signed at lower right
Lent by Mrs. Andrew Wyeth

120 ALVARO'S HAYRACK 1958

Olson Farm, South Cushing

Dry brush   8¾ x 23¼ inches   Signed at lower right
Lent by William A. Farnsworth Library and Art Museum, Rockland, Me.

121 WILD BEES 1958

The woods on N. C. Wyeth property

Pencil drawing   22⅜ x 12⅝ inches
Lent by Mrs. Andrew Wyeth

● **122 THE MILL 1958**

Brinton's Mill before restoration

Dry brush   12 x 22¼ inches
Lent by Mrs. Andrew Wyeth

123 WINTER BEES 1959

On his return from Maine, Wyeth found this nest one day on a walk through his mother's woods. He could hear the bees inside and the gold of the comb delighted him; but an animal got at the comb and destroyed it before the drawing was finished.

Dry brush drawing   21 x 27 inches   Signed at lower right
Lent by Mrs. Andrew Wyeth

124 MILL BUILDINGS 1959

Brinton's Mill before restoration

Pencil drawing   15 x 21¾ inches   Signed at lower right
Lent by Mrs. Andrew Wyeth

• **125 FUNGUS 1959**

On the path to Adam Johnson's house

Watercolor   29¾ x 21½ inches   Signed at lower right
Lent by Mr. and Mrs. J. Bruce Bredin, Greenville, Del.

126 RACE GATE 1959

At Brinton's Mill

Watercolor   13 x 20 inches   Signed at upper left
Lent by Mr. and Mrs. Leslie P. Ogden, Harrison, N. Y.
(Philadelphia and New York)

127 GERMAN POLICE DOG 1959

A study for *Ground Hog Day* (No.130), although in the end the dog was omitted,
in Karl Kuerner's kitchen

Dry brush and pencil drawing   22¼ x 16¾ inches
Lent by Mrs. Andrew Wyeth

128 FIRST SNOW 1959

Karl Kuerner's house in the first snow. The big log in the foreground turned into
a detail for *Ground Hog Day* (No.130)

Dry brush   13⅜ x 21½ inches   Signed at lower left
Lent by The Wilmington Society of the Fine Arts, The Phelps Collection,
Wilmington, Del.

129 LOG CHAIN 1959

A study of the same log

Watercolor   14¼ x 20¼ inches   Signed at lower right
Lent by Mr. and Mrs. Oscar B. Huffman, Santa Fe, N. Mex.

69

● **130 GROUND HOG DAY 1959**

Karl Kuerner's kitchen

Tempera   31 x 31 inches   Signed at middle right
Lent by Philadelphia Museum of Art (Philadelphia)

131 BEAN POLES 1959

On the road to Hoffses, Waldoboro, Maine

Watercolor   19 x 27 inches   Signed at lower right
Lent by Mr. and Mrs. Courtlandt P. Dixon, Lawrence, L.I.

132 THE STALL 1959

Olson barn

Watercolor $20\frac{1}{2}$ x $29\frac{1}{2}$ inches
Lent by Mr. Halleck Lefferts, Woodstock, Vt.

133 BLUE MEASURE 1959

Olson barn

Dry brush drawing $21\frac{7}{16}$ x $14\frac{15}{16}$ inches   Signed at lower right
Lent by Mrs. Andrew Wyeth

134 JERRY 1959

Preliminary study for *Albert's Son* (No.135)

Watercolor and pencil drawing $10\frac{1}{4}$ x $8\frac{1}{2}$ inches   Signed at upper left
Lent by Mrs. Andrew Wyeth

● **135 ALBERT'S SON 1959**

Albert Stone's barn, Cushing

Tempera   29½ x 24 inches   Signed at lower right
Lent by National Gallery of Oslo, Norway

136 CHICKEN MASH 1959

Olson woodshed

Watercolor   29 x 20½ inches   Signed at lower right
Lent by Mr. and Mrs. Vincent de Roulet, Manhasset, L.I.

137 WOLF RIVERS 1959

Wyeth picked these apples from a tree on his place in Maine and brought them
to his wife for a pie; but they had no taste, so she put them in a basket to serve
as decoration for the house. Sitting down to write to Nicky in school, Wyeth was
struck by the glow of the apples in the late afternoon light and made a quick
watercolor of them on the letter paper, then did this tempera.

Tempera   13¾ x 13 inches   Signed at lower right
Lent Anonymously

138 ETTA 1959

Etta Johnson drawn from life

Pencil drawing   21⅞ x 13⅞ inches   Signed at lower right
Lent by Mrs. Andrew Wyeth

139 ADAM 1959

Adam Johnson drawn from life

Pencil drawing   13⅞ x 21½ inches   Signed at lower right
Lent by Mrs. Andrew Wyeth

140 TOM AND HIS DAUGHTER 1959

Tom is *Tom Clark* (No.100) drawn from life at Tom Clark's house

Pencil drawing   16 x 22¼ inches   Signed at lower right
Lent by Mrs. Andrew Wyeth

141 NEGRO HAND 1959

The hand is that of *Tom Clark* (see Nos.100,140,147) drawn from life

Pencil drawing   13 x 18¼ inches   Signed at lower right
Lent by Mrs. Andrew Wyeth

73

142 SLIPPERS 1959

A study for *That Gentleman* (No.147) drawn in Tom Clark's kitchen

Pencil drawing   21 x 13½ inches   Signed at lower right
Lent by Mrs. Andrew Wyeth

143 UP IN THE WOODS 1960

The N. C. Wyeth woods

Watercolor   21½ x 29¾ inches   Signed at lower right
Lent by Amanda K. Berls, New York

144 THE DAM 1960

At Brinton's Mill

Watercolor   10⅜ x 14½ inches   Signed at lower left
Lent by Mrs. Andrew Wyeth

145 MARCH STORM 1960

Barn beside the artist's studio, Chadds Ford

Watercolor   16 x 10¹³⁄₁₆ inches   Signed at lower right
Lent by The Wilmington Society of the Fine Arts, Phelps Collection,
Wilmington, Del.

146 SNOW SHOE 1960

The N. C. Wyeth woods

Watercolor   20 x 28 inches   Signed at lower right
Lent by Mrs. John H. Hinman, Pelham, N.Y. (New York)

• **147 THAT GENTLEMAN 1960**

The grave dignity of Tom Clark (Nos.100,108,140,141,142) interested Wyeth
greatly. He is the subject of a number of paintings yet the artist is not satisfied
that he ever really caught the man's special quality: long, lean, lanky and of
immense dignity. "I learned so much from him," he observed. "He was totally
uneducated yet wise in the ways of country people." Various theories of the origin
of the Moors of Delaware have been advanced—that they were descendants of
the crew of an Arab slave ship, or of the crew of a wrecked Spanish vessel who
intermarried with Indians, or are a mixture of Indian and Negro. No one really
knows. Tom Clark's brother worked for N. C. Wyeth and the old man had been
a familiar figure to the artist from childhood. Painted in Tom Clark's kitchen.

Tempera   23½ x 47¾ inches   Signed at lower left
Lent by Dallas Museum of Fine Arts

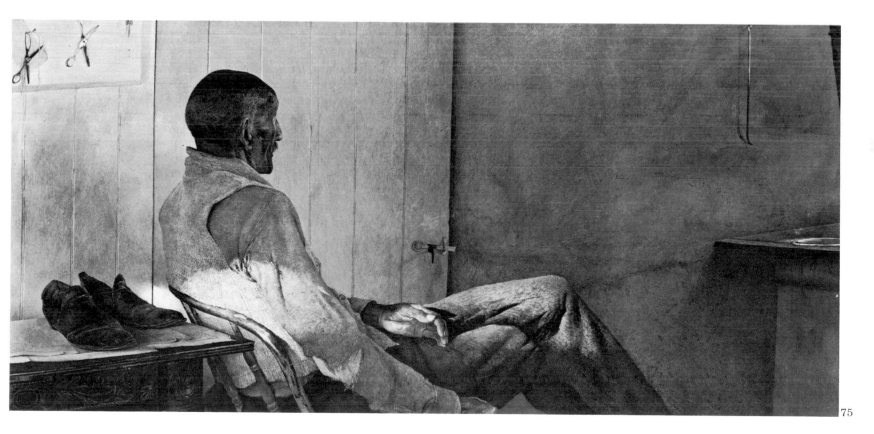

148 BELOW THE KITCHEN 1960

Painted at Kuerner farm

"Below the kitchen" is where Karl Kuerner hangs his meat. The glistening surface of the smoked ham, the strip of fresh-cut bacon with a white sliver of the fat hanging free, fascinated the painter's eye. It is one of Wyeth's rare pictures done in artificial light.

Dry brush   22¾ x 18 inches   Signed at lower left
Lent by Private American Collection

● **149 MAY DAY 1960**

The millrace at Brinton's Mill

Watercolor   12½ x 29 inches   Signed at lower right
Lent by Mrs. Andrew Wyeth

150 FLAG DAY 1960

At Tom Clark's house

Watercolor drawing   13¾ x 21¾ inches   Signed at lower right
Lent by Mrs. Andrew Wyeth

151 CAPE FORCHU LIGHT 1960

Yarmouth, Nova Scotia

Watercolor   22½ x 30¾ inches   Signed at lower left
Lent by Mr. and Mrs. Henry Sage Goodwin, Avon, Conn.

152 GERANIUMS 1960

A glimpse through the window of Christina Olson's house, of a spot of color, where the sunlight fell on the geraniums. To look through two windows, past bright objects indoors and out to the sea beyond, was an interesting painter's problem which Wyeth solved without being what he calls "tricky."

Dry brush   20¾ x 15⁹⁄₁₆ inches   Signed at lower right
Lent by Mrs. Andrew Wyeth

153 NICK 1960

Prestudy for *Above the Narrows*. Drawn from life, Cushing, Maine

Dry brush drawing   13 x 10 inches   Signed at lower right
Lent by Mrs. Andrew Wyeth

154 SMALL CRAFT WARNING 1960

Harbor at Port Clyde, Maine

Watercolor   20 x 26 inches   Signed at lower left
Lent by Mrs. John S. Griswold, Greenwich, Conn.

155 RATTLER 1960

Rattler is one of the Wyeths' dogs who also appears in *Distant Thunder* (No.169). Done in the woods at Pleasant Point, Maine.

Watercolor   21½ x 29¾ inches   Signed at lower right
Lent by Mr. and Mrs. Eugene McDermott, Dallas, Texas

● 156 YOUNG BULL 1960

Wyeth has often said that dry brush is a hard medium to control: sometimes it works out well, sometimes not. This one began as a study of the animal's eye which interested him; went on to the head, the animal, the building above. As it turned out, he feels it is very true to Karl Kuerner's in wintertime: it is a kind of heir to *Brown Swiss* (No.107). Finished just before Christmas it was a Christmas present to his wife. Done in Karl Kuerner's barnyard.

Dry brush   19¾ x 41¼ inches   Signed at lower right
Lent by Mrs. Andrew Wyeth

157 ABOVE ARCHIE'S 1961

Hill below Adam Johnson's house

Watercolor drawing   16¾ x 28 inches   Signed at lower right
Lent by Mrs. Andrew Wyeth

158 MILK CANS 1961

Adam Johnson's farm

This study of Adam Johnson's milk cans, done one very cold morning in March as a study in pale gold and silver, is an example of how beautiful the muted notes of Wyeth's tonal harmonies can be.

Dry brush drawing (with a few strokes of wash made as notes for the pale silver tone of the hill).   13¼ x 20¾ inches   Signed at lower right
Lent by Mrs. Andrew Wyeth

159 LENAPE BARN 1961

Barn across from Brinton's Mill

Watercolor   29½ x 22 inches   Signed at upper left
Lent by Dr. Margaret I. Handy, Chadds Ford, Pa.

160 HANGING DEER 1961

Study for *Tenant Farmer* (No.162). Route 1 south of Chadds Ford

Dry brush drawing   21¼ x 13½ inches   Signed at lower right
Lent by Mrs. Andrew Wyeth

161 BRICK HOUSE 1961

Study for *Tenant Farmer* (No.162)

Dry brush drawing   13½ x 21 inches
Lent by Mrs. Andrew Wyeth

162 TENANT FARMER 1961

An old brick house on the road from Chadds Ford to Kennett Square, which is said to date back to William Penn's time, was occupied by poor white tenants. Passing one winter day, Wyeth saw a deer hung up to be gutted. The snow came and covered up all the mess below. The scene haunted the artist. The dignity of the old house, the squalor of its tenants, the beauty of the wild animal, the pure cold concealing snow made an unforgettable impression upon the artist as it does upon the observer.

Tempera   30½ x 40 inches   Signed at lower right
Lent by The Wilmington Society of the Fine Arts, the Phelps Collection,
Wilmington, Del.

163 GRAIN BARREL 1961

Interior of Brinton's Mill

Watercolor   22½ x 31 inches   Signed at lower left
Lent by W. B. Connor Foundation, Danbury, Conn.

● **164 PERPETUAL CARE 1961**

This old Maine church at Wylie's corner, St. George, Maine, is the same in which *Toll Rope* (No.49) was painted. The contrast between the faded artificial flowers and the real flowers in the grass struck the artist's eye and appealed to his love of such contrasts.

Dry brush   28 x 22¾ inches   Signed at lower right
Lent anonymously (Philadelphia, Baltimore and New York)

165 BURNING OFF 1961

Fred Olson's Barn, South Cushing

Watercolor   29 x 23 inches   Signed at lower right
Lent by Mrs. Norman B. Woolworth, New York

166 SLEEP 1961

Study for *Distant Thunder* (No.169). Field behind artist's home, South Cushing

Dry brush   19¾ x 27¾ inches
Lent by Mrs. Andrew Wyeth

167 BLUEBERRIES 1961

Study for *Distant Thunder* (No.169). Painted from life

Watercolor   11¾ x 17½ inches   Signed at lower right
Lent Anonymously (Philadelphia, Baltimore and New York)

168 BROWN HAT 1961

Study for *Distant Thunder* (No.169). Artist's home, Cushing, Maine

Watercolor   11½ x 17⅜ inches   Signed at lower left
Lent by Mrs. Andrew Wyeth

• **169** DISTANT THUNDER 1961

His wife, says Wyeth, is a wonderful berry picker and he always wished to paint her picking berries. One afternoon he wandered up to the field behind their house and saw her asleep there. It was a clear afternoon; but as distant thunder rumbled over near Thomaston, Rattler's head popped out of the grass. It was just like that, the artist says, even to the spruce stem that a porcupine had gnawed bare, and Rattler's ears cocked listening to the thunder. Wyeth made it into this image of the peace of a summer afternoon.

Tempera   47½ x 30 inches   Signed at lower right
Lent by Mrs. Norman B. Woolworth, New York

170 QUART AND A HALF 1961

On the Wyeth land in Maine

Watercolor   21½ x 29¾ inches   Signed at lower right
Lent by Dr. and Mrs. James Semans, Durham, N.C.

171 NEHMI FARM 1961

Nehmi Farm is in Cushing

Watercolor   21½ x 29¾ inches   Signed at lower right
Lent by Mr. and Mrs. Marshall Field III, Chicago (New York and Chicago)

172 HAWK MOUNTAIN 1961

West Rockport, Maine

Watercolor   21½ x 29¼ inches   Signed at lower left
Lent by Mr. Halleck Lefferts, Woodstock, Vt.

173 WRITING CHAIR 1961

Bedroom in the granary, Brinton's Mill

Dry brush 20⅝ x 13¼ inches   Signed at lower left
Lent by Mrs. Andrew Wyeth

174 THE GRANARY 1961

Brinton's Mill

Watercolor 13⅝ x 21⅝ inches   Signed at lower right
Lent by Mrs. Andrew Wyeth

175 KITCHEN GARDEN 1962

The garden at Kuerner's. Wyeth likes the contrasts of things. The kitchen garden, which is women's work, even in the winter cold seems to have the warmth and intimacy of a woman's world, in contrast to the distant cattle and the fields where men work. This was a study for a tempera which never materialized.

Dry brush 23 x 22 inches
Lent by Mr. and Mrs. John T. Landreth, Lake Forest, Ill.

176 AFTER THE FLOOD 1962

Study for *The Mill* (No.178)

Pencil drawing 14½ x 28¾ inches   Signed at lower right
Lent by Mrs. Andrew Wyeth

177 STUDY FOR THE MILL 1962

Study for *The Mill* (No.178)

Watercolor 21¼ x 29½ inches   Signed at lower right
Lent by Mr. and Mrs. Walter H. Annenberg, Wynnewood, Pa.

178 THE MILL 1962

At Brinton's Mill. The family had moved to Brinton's Mill at this time but were living in the granary, which had been reroofed and made habitable while they rebuilt the house.

Tempera 30½ x 51½ inches Signed at lower left
Lent by Mr. and Mrs. Walter H. Annenberg, Wynnewood, Pa.

● **179 LIME BANKS 1962**

A lime deposit near Thomaston, Maine, is one of the town's industries which was originally developed by General Henry Knox, Washington's Chief of Artillery and the town's most famous citizen. The gleaming white banks made the artist think of Knox's white house and his white ruffles in the portrait by Stuart. The banks and the seashells in the grass across the top are white and dry; both of these qualities are interesting to Wyeth to paint.

Tempera 26¾ x 51⅝ inches Signed at lower right
Lent by Mr. Smith W. Bagley, Winston-Salem, N.C. (Philadelphia and Baltimore)

● **180 GARRET ROOM** 1962

Tom Clark's bedroom. Tom Clark (see Nos.100,108,140,141,142,147,150,181, 182) asleep on a silk patchwork quilt which his grandmother made.

Dry brush   17½ x 22½ inches   Signed at lower left
Lent by Mrs. Andrew Wyeth

181 WAITING FOR McGINLEY 1962

In Tom Clark's house

Watercolor 14¾ x 21¾ inches   Signed at upper right
Lent by Joseph H. Hirshhorn Collection, New York

182 CHESTER COUNTY 1962

The last painting of *Citizen Clark* (No.108), who has since died, upstairs in his room seated in a Morris chair. The room and the man each seem a part of and characteristic of Chester County, the small section of the earth which Wyeth has made his own.

Dry brush   22½ x 30¾ inches   Signed at lower right
Lent by Mr. and Mrs. William S. Cook, Tenant Harbor, Me.

183 WESSAWESKEAG 1962

South Thomaston, Maine

Watercolor   20⅜ x 28½ inches   Signed at lower right
Lent by Mr. Parker Poe, Camden, Me.

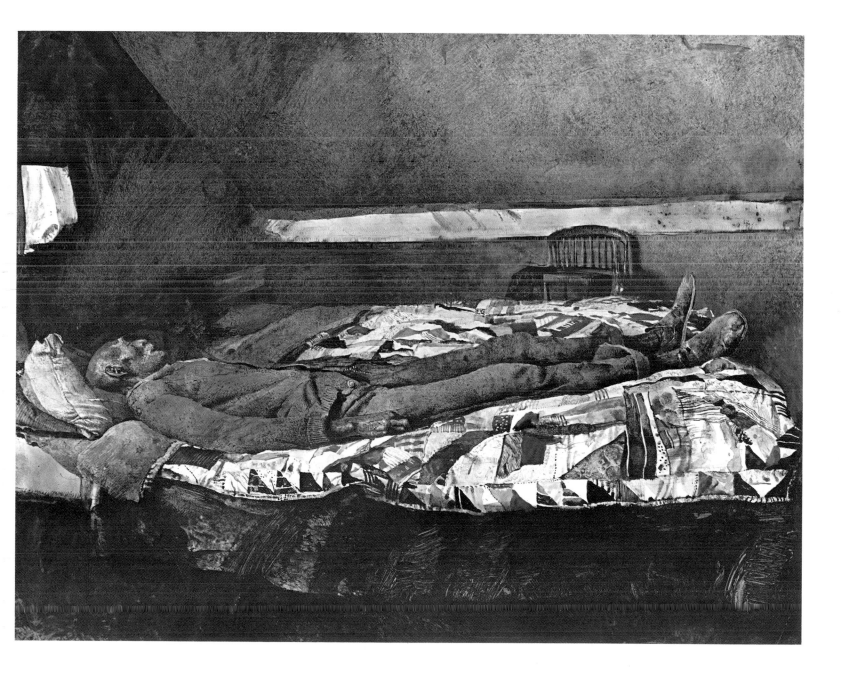

184 BACK PASTURE 1962

Behind the artist's home in Maine

Watercolor   23¾ x 18¹⁵⁄₁₆ inches
Lent by Cincinnati Art Museum

185 WOOD STOVE 1962

Christina Olson's kitchen in Maine. Wyeth wanted to make a record for himself of exactly how that room looked, and to catch the quality of *use* in all the things in it. These are Alvaro's hat and chairs; Alvaro dislikes to pose and would not be painted.

Dry brush   13⅝ x 26⅞ inches
Lent by William A. Farnsworth Library and Art Museum, Rockland, Me.

186 SHEEP FENCE 1962

Mosquito Island, Maine

Watercolor   19 x 30 inches   Signed at lower right
Lent by Mr. and Mrs. Courtland P. Dixon, Lawrence, L.I.

187 LAWN CHAIR 1962

The artist's home, Maine

Watercolor   22 x 15 inches   Signed at lower right
Lent by Mrs. Charles S. Payson, New York

188 OUTBUILDINGS 1963

Adam Johnson's farm

Watercolor   20½ x 29½ inches
Lent by Dr. and Mrs. Louis Lapid, Mt. Vernon, N.Y.

● **189 FUR HAT 1963**

Drawing for *Adam* (No.190). Drawn from life at Adam Johnson's farm

Watercolor   15¾ x 23¼ inches   Signed at lower right
Lent by Mrs. Andrew Wyeth

190 ADAM 1963

Adam Johnson lives on Kuerner's Hill just up the road from Mother Archie's Church. Wyeth goes there often in his walks, has painted many subjects around the place, and a bond of long familiarity and affection exists between the two men. Once Adam said, "I feel about you as a brother, Andy." One afternoon in late winter, Wyeth found the old man cleaning out his pigpen, getting it ready for the next year's litter. Adam is very deaf and did not hear Wyeth's approach but came slowly down the slope, a frown of concentration on his face. A flight of starlings flew like black arrowheads up into the sky. Wyeth made the sketch (No.189), of this moment of experience. Later, deciding there was something grand and elemental in the old man's figure, painted the tempera.

Tempera   24½ x 48 inches   Signed at lower left
Lent by Private American Collection

191 THE TROPHY 1963

Side of Karl Kuerner's house

Dry brush   22⅜ x 30⅓ inches   Signed at lower right
Lent by Mr. Tate Brown, New York (Philadelphia and New York)

192 EARLY SPRING 1963

N. C. Wyeth orchard, Chadds Ford

Watercolor   30 x 21¾ inches   Signed at lower left
Lent by Mr. and Mrs. Samuel F. B. Morse, Pebble Beach, Cal.

193 WASH BUCKET 1963

The granary Brinton's Mill

Watercolor   21 x 28 inches   Signed at lower left
Lent by Mrs. Thomas S. Kelly, New York

● 194 MAY 23RD 1963

South Hope, Maine

Watercolor   22 x 30 inches   Signed at lower right
Lent by Mr. and Mrs. Stephen W. Blodgett, Garrison, N.Y.

- **195 DAY OF THE FAIR 1963**

Painted in artist's Chadds Ford studio

This is *Granddaughter* (No.96) seven years later, dressed to go to the fair that afternoon and suffering from fifteen-year-old shyness. Today she plans to go to West Chester State College and will be, the artist believes, a handsome and dignified woman.

Dry brush   15 x 20 inches   Signed at lower left
Lent by City Art Museum of St. Louis

196 HER ROOM 1963

Painted in the front room of their place in Maine, the room which to the artist is very much a part and expression of his wife. The late afternoon light across the room is always beautiful; the wind comes up then, ruffling the blue of the river. One day, when the wind came up strongly and worried the artist for his two boys out sailing on the river, suddenly the front door slammed and fixed the moment in his mind.

Tempera $24^{11}/_{16}$ x 48 inches   Signed at upper right
Lent by William A. Farnsworth Library and Art Museum, Rockland, Me.

IV. *THE NEW PHASE*

Somewhere about this time Wyeth's work seems to me to have entered a new phase. Portraits of people in life size, rather than as elements in a landscape, come to the fore, revealing new powers of penetrating observation and feeling. Dry brush watercolors become deeper and richer in tone, more compact and concentrated in composition. All the qualities of his earlier work are there but are now intensified. The precise beginning of this new phase is hard to define but the first work which seems to belong wholly to it is:

● **197 THE DRIFTER 1964**

Painted in artist's Chadds Ford studio

Willard Snowden had been in the navy and the merchant marine, had seen much of the world and done many things, drifting through life until chance brought him to Wyeth and to a job taking care of the studio. With this portrait Wyeth added a new dimension to his understanding of and power to paint human beings.

Dry brush   22½ x 28½ inches   Signed at upper right
Lent by Mrs. Andrew Wyeth

● **198 THE BACHELOR 1964**

Christian C. Sanderson's side porch, Chadds Ford

Watercolor   30 x 22 inches   Signed at lower right
Lent by Mrs. Lee C. Schlesinger, Metairie, La.

199 FARM WAGONS 1964

Brinton's Mill

Study for *Marsh Hawk* (No.200)

Pencil drawing   19½ x 39¾ inches   Signed at lower right
Lent by Mrs. Andrew Wyeth

200 MARSH HAWK 1964

Brinton's Mill again, painted in the last light of day. The artist has caught the feeling of the last moments of sunlight before the shadow of the western hills covers the valley bottom.

Tempera   30½ x 45 inches
Lent by Dr. Margaret I. Handy, Chadds Ford, Pa.

201 NETHER STONE 1964

Brinton's Mill

Watercolor   29½ x 21 inches   Signed at lower right
Lent by Mr. and Mrs. Andrew J. Sordoni, Jr., Forty-Fort, Pa.

202 BERRY BUCKET 1964

Wyeth's kitchen, Cushing, Maine

Watercolor   28 x 20 inches
Lent by Mr. and Mrs. Robert Montgomery, New York

● **203** THE PATRIOT 1964

Ralph Kline, who runs a sawmill in Spruce Head, Maine, is an old friend of the artist. The picture was painted in late autumn in the loft of the sawmill; the air was full of the smell of spruce lumber and wood smoke. Kline is descended from pre-Revolutionary German settlers in Waldoboro and has Indian blood also. To Wyeth, he is the type of man who would have fought at Concord Bridge; as he sat for his portrait, he talked of France and the 1914 war. It gave Ralph Kline great pleasure to wear his old uniform again: Sergeant York was his hero. The artist has painted with great sensitivity not only the character of the old veteran but the way his figure, though vital and strong, now does not quite fill his uniform, and the scratchiness of OD cloth in contrast to the soft dry skin of an old man.

Tempera   27½ x 23½ inches   Signed at upper left
Lent by Mrs. Andrew Wyeth

204 MILK ROOM 1964

Karl Kuerner's barn

Watercolor   30 x 22 inches   Signed at lower left
Lent by Mrs. Lee C. Schlesinger, Metairie, La.

205 MOVED OUT 1964

Empty room in the artist's studio, Chadds Ford

Watercolor   28¼ x 23¾ inches   Signed at lower right
Lent by Mr. and Mrs. Raymond French, Locust Valley, L.I.

206 OUT OF SERVICE 1964

Monhegan Island, Maine

Watercolor   22¾ x 29 inches   Signed at lower left
Lent by Mr. and Mrs. Robert Blum, Old Westbury, L.I.

207 THE WAKE 1964

The scene is the Georges River in Maine. The artist has caught the peculiar color and translucence of a tidal river whose moving water holds mud in it, and the feeling of a boat charging, running wild and free.

Tempera   30 x 48 inches   Signed at lower right
Lent by Mr. and Mrs. William E. Weiss, Jr., New York (Philadelphia and New York)

208 V.F.W. 1964

Back of Ralph Kline's house

Watercolor   29¾ x 21½ inches   Signed at lower left
Lent by M. Knoedler and Co., Inc., New York

• **209 UP IN THE STUDIO 1965**

A portrait of the artist's sister, Carolyn, in her studio at Chadds Ford. The artist painted her as he found her, one day, sitting by the studio window and looking at the woods she loves so well. The picture speaks of the whole quality of a life.

Dry brush   17 x 23⅞ inches   Signed at lower right
Lent by Amanda K. Berls, New York (Philadelphia, New York and Chicago)

210 THE COUNTRY 1965

The Brinton's Mill house needed to be rebuilt inside and out before the family could move from the Granary into their new home. The artist's wife, Betsy, planned, supervised, furnished the house with love and great taste: it is her creation and is both old and new. One fresh winter morning the artist saw her looking out of one of the windows. The new wood of the new window framed her: fresh, confident, gay; and so he painted her.

Tempera   40 x 30 inches   Signed at lower left
Lent by Virginia Museum of Fine Arts, Richmond

211 AFTER THE CHASE 1965

Painted at Brinton's Mill

Watercolor   27½ x 19   Signed at lower left
Lent by Mr. and Mrs. Lee E. Phillips, Jr., Wichita, Kan.

212 CHAIN HOIST 1965

Brinton's Mill

Watercolor   20 x 27½ inches
Lent by Mrs. Alfred E. Bissell, Wilmington, Del.

213 MONOLOGUE 1965

Painted in artist's Chadds Ford studio

Willard, with his dark and bearded face, is rather an alarming figure to some Chadds Ford people. He is in truth timid and retiring, unable to cope with the world. He keeps the shutters closed in the part of the studio which he inhabits, and moves like a shadow in the darkness. It is easy to see why his brown-gold figure in the dim light would appeal to an artist's eye. But why call it *Monologue?* —"Because he talked all the time while he was sitting." About what?—"Oh, about wine, mostly. He was worried about holidays. 'They should be kind to the human race,' he said to me. 'They should have the package stores open on Easter.' "

Dry brush   22¼ x 28½ inches   Signed at lower right
Lent by Mr. and Mrs. William E. Weiss, Jr., New York (Philadelphia and New York)

● **214 DUE BACK 1965**

Teel's Island

Watercolor   18½ x 23½ inches
Lent by Mr. Stanley S. Snellenburg, Philadelphia

215 CUT GRANITE **1965**

Below Marshall Point Light, Port Clyde

Watercolor   27¾ x 19 inches   Signed at upper left
Lent by Mr. Robert H. Smith, Bethesda, Md.

216 WASH HOUSE **1965**

Marshall Point Light, Port Clyde

Watercolor   29¾ x 21½ inches   Signed at upper right
Lent by Mr. and Mrs. Lester Avnet, Great Neck, N.Y.

● **217** WEATHER SIDE **1965**

Olson Farm

"I've had some sad experiences," said Wyeth. "Things disappear before I can get to them." That is the reason behind this exact portrait of the Olson house. Like Tenant Farmer (No.162) it is a very real picture of the personality of a house. Each detail, each window has a life of its own. The weathered clapboards in the sunlight are bathed in bright light; yet the house had to appear both solid and hollow, firm yet destined perhaps to disappear.

Tempera   48 x 28 inches
Lent by Mr. and Mrs. Alexander M. Laughlin, New York   (New York)

218 STORM AT SEA 1965

Sea gulls below the lighthouse on Pemaquid Point, painted on a cold, forbidding day. There was a storm offshore and the gulls, instead of putting to sea, remained snuggled on the ground, their backs to the ocean. The brooding light, the spindrift in the air, the mood of hush before the storm, are caught with great subtlety. It is characteristic of Wyeth's mind that he prefers to imply the storm without painting it: a sense of larger things unseen pervades the small detail he portrays for us.

Dry brush   19½ x 39¼ inches   Signed at lower left
Lent by Mrs. Andrew Wyeth

● **219 THE PIKES 1965**

Brinton's Mill

Watercolor   27⅛ x 19 inches   Signed at upper left
Lent by Mr. and Mrs. Norton S. Walbridge, La Jolla, Cal. (Philadelphia, Baltimore and New York)

- **220** RIVER VALLEY 1966

Brinton's Mill

Watercolor   21¼ x 26½ inches   Signed at lower right
Lent by Mrs. Andrew Wyeth

221 MAGA'S DAUGHTER 1966

Living room of Wyeth's mill house

The Quaker eighteenth-century hat was acquired some time ago. Wyeth at
one time thought of painting a still life of it. When his wife put on the hat one
day, the effect delighted him and this portrait is the result. One of the remarkable pictures of his latest and most mature phase, it characteristically unites
past and present—his wife's face and her resemblance to her mother (see the
Chambered Nautilus, No.99); the charm of life and the charm of past Quaker
ladies who knew how becoming to a pretty face their costume could be.

Tempera   26½ x 30¼ inches   Signed at lower right
Lent by Mr. Andrew Wyeth

● 222 GRAPE WINE 1966

In artist's Chadds Ford studio

The difference between Willard's face in *The Drifter* of 1964 and here tells a sad story. But with what skill and subtlety the artist has painted both the changed personality and the altered face. This is the life of a human being, presented with mature artistry by an extraordinary observer.

Tempera   25⅞ x 29⅛ inches   Signed at upper left
Lent by M. Knoedler & Co., Inc., New York

This is the story of Andrew Wyeth's work until today. Happily there is more to come.

EDGAR P. RICHARDSON
WINTERTHUR, DELAWARE – JUNE 1, 1966

INDEX

Published by Abercrombie & Fitch Co., New York, N.Y.

Typography by Typographic Service Inc., Philadelphia, Pa.

Color Plates by Graphic Color Plate Co., Stamford, Conn.